D1190104

What I Love about Mom

I love your

_____ .

I love hearing stories about your

_____ .

3

You inspire me to

_____ .

I love it when you call me

_____ .

I'm humbled by your

_____ .

I love remembering the time we went

_____

with

_____ .

I'm thankful I got your

_____ .

I love that you still

_____

for me.

I hope to be as

_____

as you one day.

I am so

_____

that

_____ .

I love how you never

_____ .

I love how you always

_____ .

13

When I was little, I loved to watch you

_____

in the

_____ .

If I had to describe you
in one word, it'd be

_____ .

I'd love it if we could

_____

together soon.

If you were a dance, you'd be the

_____ .

I love getting your advice on

_____ .

You have the prettiest

_____ .

I never get tired of your

_____ .

I love how you never get tired of my

_____ .

You are so

_____ .

You are so

_____ .

You are so

_____ .

If you were a scent, you'd be

_____ .

23

I love that you encourage me to

_____ .

24

Sometimes your ability to

_____

amazes me.

It makes me laugh to think how you

_____ .

I'd be lost without your

_____ .

27

I love that you taught me

_____ .

28

You

_____

the best

_____

ever.

I love how good you are at

_____ .

30

When we are apart, it makes me
happy to think about

_____ .

31

I wish I had known you when

_____ .

32

I love going to

_____

with you.

33

I love your taste in

_____ .

I hope you get to

_____

your favorite

_____

soon.

If you wanted to, you could easily

_____ .

I have to admit
you're always right about

_____ .

I love that

_____

you used to wear.

I admire your dedication to

_____ .

You deserve the

_____

award.

I love the sound of your

_____

when you

_____ .

I love that you love my

_____ .

I love to play

_____

with you.

I still can't believe you

_____ .

44

I love it when you

_____

like

_____

I love how you have such strong

_____ .

I always want to hear what
you're going to say about

_____ .

It makes me smile when you

_____ .

48

I love to

_____

for you.

Nobody else can

_____

like you.

Thank you for

I Love You, Mom.